W9-ANG-348

PRIMARY
PAK
Practice, Apply & Know

JULY
We Discover Our World

Level 1

Printed in U.S.A.
ISBN: 0-395-81035-3
456789-B-99 98

Houghton Mifflin Company • Boston
Atlanta • Dallas • Geneva, Illinois • Palo Alto • Princeton

Home/School Involvement Masters-July

Home and School Involvement resources are provided for each theme/month.

The Family Newsletter introduces the theme, highlighting the topics to be introduced during the next month's program. Each newsletter includes a short bibliography of recommended books that parents can share with their children. These are current titles available at most public libraries.

The Family Newsletter should be sent home at the launch of the theme so that parents and children can share in the theme.

The Home Activities Master provides parents with simple, but rich, experiences that support the social studies program. Through sharing the curriculum in the home, children better understand the importance and the lifelong relevance of learning about people and events over time.

The home activities have been designed to provide interesting family activities that support learning. By sharing experiences both at home and in school, children become much more motivated learners.

The Family Newsletter and Home Activities Master are only a small part of oral and written communication between home and school. However, these resources provide an important beginning to home/school involvement.

Home/School Involvement Masters for July:

Social Studies Family Newsletter

Our next social studies theme is called . . .

July: We Discover Our World

We'll be learning about . . .

The Fourth of July

We'll explore how Americans celebrate their country's birthday—complete with a parade!

Travel

Summertime often means travel. We'll look at travel long ago and now, and talk about what a family on a coast-to-coast trip might see.

People Moving People

We'll find out about the different people—airplane pilots, bus drivers, train engineers, ship captains—who make moving from place to place possible.

Ways of Getting Around

We'll learn about different modes of transportation—in the air, on (and in) the water, and on city streets.

Here are some resources to help you explore the theme at home:

Books

Reflections by Ann Jonas
A child goes to the seashore but returns to enjoy a concert with his family all in the same day.

Round Trip by Ann Jonas
Innovative illustrations capture the motion of a round trip.

Paul Revere's Ride by Henry Wadsworth Longfellow
Illustrator Nancy Winslow Parker makes this famous piece accessible to young readers.

Social Studies Home Activities

July: We Discover Our World

While we celebrate the Fourth of July and modern mobility in class, you can try some of these activities at home to help your child understand the theme.

Happy Birthday, USA!

As your child's class learns about ways we celebrate the birth of the United States on July 4, 1776, you might enjoy working together to make a special birthday hat for the occasion. Use stiff paper and tape or staples. Before you put the hat together, though, invite your child to decorate it with drawings, glue and glitter, and streamers. Be sure to use red, white, and blue! When it's finished, your child might enjoy wearing the birthday hat to your community's Fourth of July parade.

Making Plans

In class, we'll be talking about some of the things people do in summer. Help your child to lay out a calendar for July and fill it with planned activities—perhaps special family events, a Fourth of July party, or a family vacation. He or she can decorate the page with summertime themes, and then draw one big picture for July. Post the calendar on the refrigerator.

On the Move

Your child will be learning about various ways of getting around. He or she might enjoy planning an imaginary coast-to-coast trip that uses as many kinds of transportation as possible—the wackier the better. If possible, consult a map of the country, and talk about ways of getting through the desert (a solar-powered skateboard, perhaps?) or across the Mississippi (a paddle boat?). Vehicles will have to be abandoned every so often—that's part of the game. Have your child keep a list of all the kinds of vehicles used, with separate columns for air-, water-, and land-based transportation.

Return Address

In class, we'll be talkng about our "global address." Your child might enjoy making some personalized stationery—a sheet of letter paper and an envelope—that includes your address and a drawing. The drawing might be a self-portrait or describe something about the place you live. Your child can then use the stationery to write a letter to a friend or relative.

Boletín informativo de estudios sociales

Nuestro próximo tema de estudios sociales se llama . . .

Julio: descubrimos nuestro mundo

Vamos a aprender sobre . . .

El 4 de julio

Exploraremos cómo celebran los norteamericanos el cumpleaños de su país, ¡terminando con un desfile!

Viajes

A menudo el verano propone un viaje. Daremos una mirada a los viajes de antes y a los de ahora y hablaremos de lo que podría ver una familia en un viaje de costa a costa.

Gente trasladando gente

Descubriremos a las diferentes personas— pilotos de avión, conductores de autobuses, ingenieros de trenes, capitanes de barcos— que hacen posible el traslado de un lado a otro.

Maneras de trasladarse

Aprenderemos sobre diferentes medios de transporte—en el aire, sobre y dentro del agua y en las calles de la ciudad.

Aquí tiene algunos recursos para ayudarle a explorar el tema en casa:

Libros

Reflections de Ann Jonas
Un niño va hasta el borde del mar pero vuelve para disfrutar de un concierto con su familia, todo en el mismo día.

Round Trip de Ann Jonas
Ilustraciones novedosas captan el movimiento de un viaje de ida y vuelta.

Paul Revere's Ride de Henry Wadsworth Longfellow
La ilustradora Nancy Winslow Parker hace accesible su famosa obra a los jóvenes lectores.

Actividades de estudios sociales en casa

Julio: descubrimos nuestro mundo

Mientras celebramos el 4 de julio y la movilidad moderna en clase, usted puede realizar en casa algunas de estas actividades para ayudar a que su niño entienda este tema.

¡Feliz cumpleaños, USA!

Mientras la clase de su niño aprende los modos de celebrar el nacimiento de los Estados Unidos el 4 de julio de 1776, ustedes pueden disfrutar haciendo juntos un sombrero especial para tal ocasión. Use papel rígido, cinta adhesiva o grapas. Asegúrense de usar los colores rojo, blanco y azul. Cuando hayan terminado, a su niño quizá le gustaría ponerse el sombrero de cumpleaños para el desfile del 4 de julio en su vecindario.

Haciendo planes

En clase, estaremos hablando sobre algunas de las cosas que hace la gente en el verano. Ayude a su niño a diseñar un calendario para julio y a llenarlo con actividades organizadas, quizás un suceso familiar especial, una fiesta del 4 de julio o una vacación con la familia. Él o ella puede decorar la página con temas veraniegos y luego hacer un gran dibujo para julio. Exhiban el calendario en la nevera.

En constante movimiento

Su niño estará aprendiendo los distintos modos de trasladarse. Él o ella puede disfrutar planeando un viaje imaginario de costa a costa que use todos los medios de transporte posibles, (cuanto más extraños, mejor). Si es posible consulten un mapa del país y hablen sobre cómo cruzar el desierto (¿una patineta a energía solar, quizás?) o el Mississippi (¿un bote de remos?). Los vehículos deben ser abandonados muy a menudo; es parte del juego. Haga que su niño lleve una lista con columnas separadas para aire, agua y tierra, de todos los tipos de vehículos que han usado.

Remitente

En clase, estaremos hablando de nuestra "dirección mundial". Su niño puede disfrutar haciendo papel de correspondencia personalizado—una hoja de papel y un sobre— que incluya su dirección y un dibujo. El dibujo puede ser un autorretrato o representar algo del lugar donde viven. Luego, su niño puede usar esto para escribir una carta a un amigo o familiar.

Skill Masters-July

WE THE PEOPLE: GROW AND CHANGE, the first-grade social studies program, provides the foundation skills for the social studies curriculum throughout elementary school. The Skill Masters for each theme are in three categories, as follows:

- Visual Skills such as using word webs, interpreting photographs, reading simple graphs, and reading a timeline.

- Research Skills such as learning to formulate good questions, reading for information (cause/effect), identifying the main idea, using a glossary, organizing events in sequence, reading for information to support generalizations, and using library resources.

- Map Skills such as interpreting a view from above; reading a picture map; reading a map key; exploring distances on a map; learning cardinal directions and map symbols; and reading community, United States, and world maps.

Each theme includes two skill workshops in the Big Books and the Teacher's Book. The Teacher's Book provides several activities for children to practice and apply what they have learned. The following masters also provide skill practice:

Skill Masters for July:

Name _____ Date _____

My Address on the Planet

Fill in the words that tell your address.

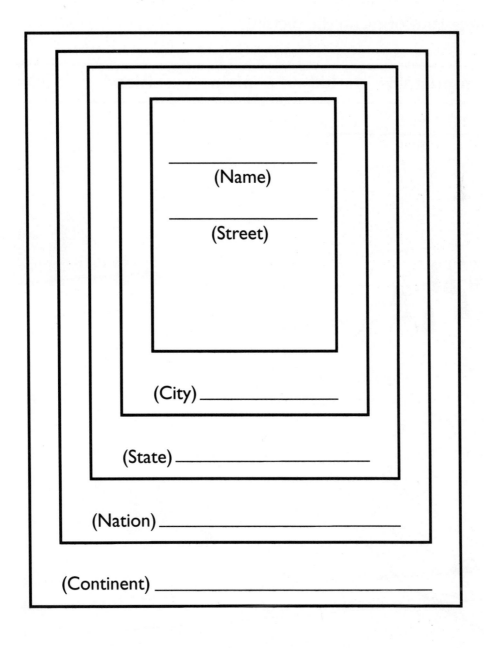

_____ (Name)

_____ (Street)

(City) _____

(State) _____

(Nation) _____

(Continent) _____

_____ (World)

Name _____ Date _____

What Am I?

Look at the picture below.

Label these landforms on the picture.

mountain	hill	plain	island	river

Activity Masters-July

WE THE PEOPLE: GROW AND CHANGE is an experience/activity-based program. The Big Book pages and the Teacher's Book provide a wide range of highly interactive, cross-curricular activities designed to involve children in the experiences of history, geography, citizenship, economics, cultures, and ethics and belief systems.

Each theme includes many activity choices to support social studies learning and to support the other curricular areas–reading/language arts, mathematics, science, and the arts. The best practice, application, and enrichment is provided in these activities, which are designated for the class, small groups, or individuals.

Several activities in the theme are supported by Activity Masters. The masters are included wherever children might be required to do the activity quickly and simply. These masters also provide materials to send home and/or include in children's portfolios.

The Activity Masters for July are as follows:

Name _____   Date _____

A Perfect Way to Get Around

Work with a friend to plan a new vehicle.

Use the questions to help you plan your vehicle.

Write about your ideas.

How will your vehicle move?

_____

How will people get in and out?

_____

Where will people sit?

_____

What will be inside?

_____

Will it have a computer? What will the computer do?

_____

Draw a picture of your perfect vehicle on the back of the page.

Name _____ Date _____

Summer Poem

Finish the sentences to write a summer poem.

My favorite thing to do in the summer is

The warm weather makes me feel

If I eat ice cream, I always feel

When I play with my friends, it makes me want to

In the summer, I always feel

Fold this page along the dotted line so the words are on the outside.

Read your summer poem!

Reading Support-July

WE THE PEOPLE: GROW AND CHANGE, as a primary-level program, is an intrinsic part of the Reading/Language Arts curriculum. At these levels we teach reading, language arts, and all the content areas as a more integrated curriculum. Teachers do not leave reading to go to social studies or math; they extend the curriculum to encompass all areas as supporting literacy.

A strong feature of Levels 1 and 2 of WE THE PEOPLE are the Reading Support pages in the Teacher's Book. For each theme, there is a wide range of activities to teach and support VOCABULARY, PHONICS, READING STRATEGIES, and WRITING.

The VOCABULARY activities reinforce key vocabulary and grade-level vocabulary. PHONICS activities provide many opportunities to support the critical phonics/word-attack skills children need at Grades 1 and 2. READING STRATEGY activities provide the range of strategies children must be able to use to comprehend what they read. Children must have these skills to access reading materials, including social studies. WRITING activities provide rich opportunities to use the social studies content in varied writing experiences.

The PRIMARY PAK for each theme/month provides masters to reinforce each of these areas.

The Teacher's Book activities, together with the masters, strongly support the Reading/Language Arts curriculum.

The Reading Support Masters for July are as follows:

Name _____ Date _____

Vocabulary

Use the words in the word bank to write or tell about the picture.

Word Bank

traffic

parade

_____

_____

_____

_____

Name _____ Date _____

Reading Strategy: Summarize

What is the most important thing you learned about
the Fourth of July? Draw and write about it here.

_____

_____

_____

Name _____   Date _____

Phonics: Contractions

Read each sentence. Draw a line under the contraction.

Write the two words that make up the contraction.

1. There's lots to see in the sky.   _____

2. You can't see a bird.   _____

3. There isn't a plane.   _____

4. Let's see what you can see!   _____

Work with a partner to name the things you see in the sky!

Name _____ Date _____

Writing

Write a poem about sounds. Think of a sound word
for each picture. Write the word on the line.

HOME SOUNDS

Dog _____**barking**_____ .

Television _____**buzzing**_____ .

Phone _____ .

Door _____ .

Feet _____ .

Kitchen pots _____ .

Assessment Masters-July

The PRIMARY PAK for JULY includes three resources to support your assessment needs. These are the Theme Test, a Theme Objectives Checklist, and a Theme Project Checklist.

Informal and formal assessment opportunities are provided for each theme. Each lesson lists objectives to be covered and provides immediate opportunities for informal assessment. Portfolio opportunities are also referenced in the lesson plans.

The Theme Test assesses the content of the theme–the big ideas and the new skills–through multiple-choice items and a range of open-ended responses. The Theme Objectives Checklist can be used throughout the program to note an individual student's progress and needs.

The Theme Project is designed as an assessment experience for children, allowing them rich opportunities to apply new knowledge and skills. The Theme Project Checklist is an excellent resource to note an individual student's knowledge and participation.

The Assessment Masters for July are as follows:

Name _____   Date _____

Theme Test

To the Teacher: Read aloud each test item. Allow time for students to respond.

Choose the best answer. Circle your choice.

1. What happens on July 4?

2. How did people travel long ago?

3. Which travels on water?

Name _____ Date _____

Now follow these directions.

4. Look at this map of the United States.

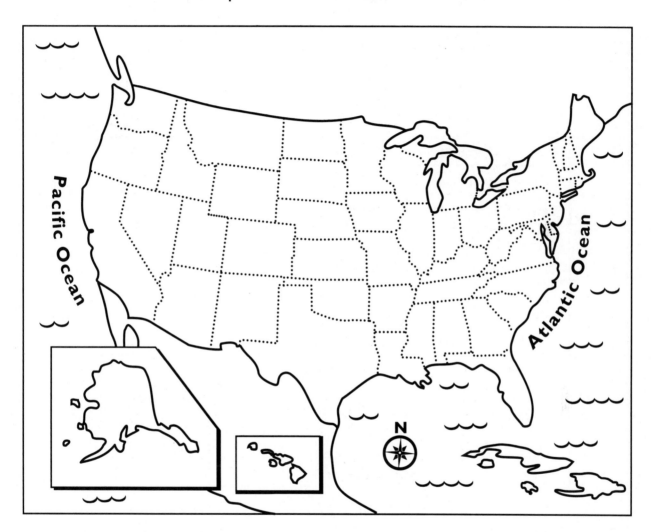

Make an **X** on the map to show where you live.

Draw a line from your **X** to an ocean.

5. Draw a picture showing three ways to travel.

Draw your picture on the back of this sheet. Tell what your

picture shows.

Theme Objectives Checklist

Listed below are the major lesson objectives of this Theme. Next to each, indicate your assessment of each student's current level of performance on the objective.

Pages	Objectives	Student Name								
1	Describes summer activities as described in poetry									
	Identifies patriotic customs of the U.S.									
2–3	States the purpose of the July 4th holiday									
4–5	Traces a route on an illustrated map									
6–7	Lists some things the Prices will see and hear on their trip									
8–9	Skill: Identifies land and water on a diagram									
10–11	Correlates transportation workers with their jobs									
12–13	Identifies differences in modes of travel throughout history									
14–15	Lists different ways of traveling by water									
16–17	Lists different ways of traveling by air									
18–19	Explains geographical location in global terms									
	Locates city, state, and nation on maps									
20	Identifies what makes "America the Beautiful" a patriotic song									

Use the following abbreviations.
P=proficient in this objective   **D**=developing skill in this objective   **E**=exploring this objective   **N**=not observed

Theme Project Checklist

To rate the child's performance on the Theme Project "Boat, Plane, and Balloon Travel," make a check mark next to each item.

Student's Name _____   Date _____

		Excellent	Good	Developing
Social Studies Content Understood	1. The child identifies various modes of transportation.			
	2. The child selects a mode of transportation suited to a planned journey.			
	3. The child reads routes, land, and water on a map.			
	4.			
Discussion	5. The child suggests a landform for class map.			
	6. The child suggests an appropriate mode of transportation.			
	7.			
Group Work on Vehicle and Map	8. The child chooses an appropriate vehicle.			
	9. The child traces a route on map.			
	10. The child describes journey referring to map.			
	11.			

One thing that the child did particularly well in this project was _____

_____

_____

_____

Overall evaluation: _____

_____

_____

_____

Signed _____

Theme Test: July

Answer Key

1. C   [pp. 2–3]

2. C   [pp. 12–13]

3. A   [pp. 14–17]

4. *X* should be in correct state close to correct location; line should connect *X* to either ocean. [pp. 4–5, 8–9, 18–19]

5. Accept any three modes of transportation for land, sea, or air travel; description should match picture. [theme wide]